The I
House

Contents

The Empty House   **4**

Thief!   **17**

Vocabulary   **31**

Story Questions   **32**

Titles in the Runway series

Level 4	Level 5	Level 6
The Street	Trapped	The Good Student
The Wish	The Rumour	Virtual Teacher
The Magic Shop	The Food Museum	Football Smash
The Ghost House	Escape from the City	The Empty House

Badger Publishing Limited
15 Wedgwood Gate, Pin Green Industrial Estate,
Stevenage, Hertfordshire SG1 4SU
Telephone: 01438 356907. Fax: 01438 747015
www.badger-publishing.co.uk
enquiries@badger-publishing.co.uk

The Empty House ISBN 978 1 84691 376 1

Publisher: David Jamieson
Commissioning Editor: Carrie Lewis
Design: Fiona Grant
Illustration: Anthony Williams, Oliver Lake, cover by Pete Smith

Printed and bound in China through Colorcraft Ltd., Hong Kong

The Empty House

Written by Alison Hawes
Illustrated by Anthony Wiliams
and Pete Smith

On the way home from school,
Josef and Dan go past an old house.
It is big and dark and empty.

One day Dan stopped in front of the empty house.

"There's a ghost in there," he said. "Sometimes, I can hear it crying."

"There isn't a ghost!" laughed Josef.

"Yes, there is!" said Dan.

"Let's go inside and see if there is a ghost then," said Josef.

"No!" said Dan.

But Josef ran off down the path.
He pushed open the door and went inside.

Dan didn't want to go inside.
But he went in behind Josef.

Inside, the house was big and dark and empty.

"See, there is no ghost!" said Josef.

"Yes, there is!" said Dan, "I can hear it crying!"

But Josef just laughed.

"Look behind you," he said.

Dan looked behind him.

"It's not a ghost! It's a cat!" said Josef.

"It got trapped in here.
It's crying to be let out," said Josef.

He pulled open the door and let the cat out.

Josef and Dan went home.
They walked back up the path.
The cat walked off in the snow.

Suddenly Dan stopped in front of Josef.

"What's the matter?" said Josef.

"Look behind you!" said Dan.

"Can you see our footprints in the snow?" said Dan.

"Yes," said Josef.

"Now look at the cat's footprints," said Dan.

"But there aren't any cat footprints," said Josef.

Josef looked at Dan.

"Ghosts don't make footprints," said Dan.

"So it's not a cat. It's a ghost!" said Josef.

"Yes!" said Dan. "The cat got trapped and died."

"Run!" said Josef.

Thief!

Written by **Alison Hawes**
Illustrated by **Oliver Lake**

Mel and Reema got the bus to the shopping centre.
They wanted to go to the mobile phone shop.

Reema saw a phone she liked.
"How much is this phone, please?" said
Reema.

"It is £200. Would you like to buy it?" said
the shop assistant.

"No, it is too expensive," said Reema. Reema put the phone back on the shelf.

"Let's go to a different shop. They might have something cheaper."

"Put the phone in your bag, Reema," said Mel.

"No! I am not a thief!" said Reema.

Mel took the phone off the shelf.
She put the phone in Reema's bag.
But Reema wasn't looking.

Mel started to walk out.
"Let's go, Reema, I want to go to the cinema," said Mel.

A security guard stopped Mel and Reema at the door.
He looked in their bags.

Reema got a big shock.
The phone she had looked at was in her bag!
She didn't know how it had got there.

The security guard let Mel leave the shop.
He took Reema to his office.
"I am calling the Police," he said.

"No! I am not a thief. I didn't take the phone. Please, check the shop cameras," said Reema.

The security guard checked the shop cameras.
He saw Mel take the phone.
He saw Mel put the phone in Reema's bag when Reema wasn't looking.

The security guard let Reema go.
But he still called the Police.

The Police went to Mel's house.
This time, Mel got a big shock!

Vocabulary

The Empty House

empty
ghost
crying
laughed
pushed
inside
behind
trapped
suddenly
footprints

Thief!

shopping centre
mobile
assistant
expensive
different
cheaper
thief
cinema
security guard
office
cameras

▶》》 Story questions

The Empty House

What does Dan say he can hear when he passes the house?
Is Josef brave to go in?
What is crying in the house?
Why doesn't the cat have footprints?

Thief!

Why does Mel put the phone in Reema's bag?
Why do you think the security guard stopped the girls?
How does Reema show that she is not a thief?
Why do you think some people steal?